WS

4752

MITTON, T.

My hat and all that

70003242408   Pbk

Please return/renew this item by the last date shown

  **worcestershire**
 c o u n t y c o u n c i l
Libraries & Learning

My Hat
and All That

Tony Mitton

Illustrated by
Sue Heap

CORGI YEARLING

MY HAT AND ALL THAT
A CORGI YEARLING BOOK : 0 440 867258

Published in Great Britain by Random House Children's Books
and David Fickling Books

This edition published 2006

1 3 5 7 9 10 8 6 4 2

Text copyright © 2006 by Tony Mitton
Illustrations copyright © 2006 by Sue Heap

Set in 13/17 pt New Baskerville
by Falcon Oast Graphic Art Ltd

Corgi Yearling Books are published by Random House Children's Books,
61–63 Uxbridge Rd, London W5 5SA, a division of The Random House Group Ltd,
in Australia by Random House Australia (Pty) Ltd,
20 Alfred Street, Milsons Point, Sydney, New South Wales 2061, Australia
in New Zealand by Random House New Zealand Ltd,
18 Poland Road, Glenfield, Auckland 10, New Zealand,
and in South Africa by Random House (Pty) Ltd, Isle of Houghton,
Corner Boundary Road & Carse O'Gowrie, Houghton 2198, South Africa

To all the children I do my gigs for,
from Tony Mitton

For Bella
S.H.

Contents

IN MY POCKET

AT MY FINGERTIPS

POEM TO RAP IT UP

UNDER MY HAT

My Hat

Here's my hat.
It holds my head,
the thoughts I've had
and the things I've read.

It keeps out the wind.
It keeps off the rain.
It hugs my hair
and warms my brain.

There's me below it,
the sky above it.
It's my lid.
And I love it.

Growing

Now, today
you may
be small.

But one day
you'll be tall,
like me,
maybe . . . taller!

You won't
fit into your bed.
Your hat
won't fit on your head.
Your feet . . .
will fill up the floor!
You'll have to bend down
to come through the door.
You'll be able to reach
the highest shelf.
And I can't do that now,
myself!

Out in the country
the tallest trees
will scratch your ankles
and tickle your knees.

Up in the clouds,
yes, way up there,
the eagles will nest
in your craggy hair.

But they'd better soon find
a safer place,
because soon your head
will be up in space!

So I hope you won't
be too proud to lean down
and say hello
to your old home town.

And I hope it won't drive you
utterly mad,
to visit your tiny
Mum and Dad.

Grown Out Of

My trousers are tight.
They just won't fit.

And my jumper?
I've grown out of it.

My shirt's too short.
It just won't do.

There are holes in my socks
where my toes peep through.

So it's lucky I don't
grow out of my skin.

'Cos then there'd be nothing
to put *me* in.

Plum

Don't be so glum,
plum.

Don't feel beaten.

You were made
to be eaten.

But don't you know
that deep within,
beneath your juicy flesh
and flimsy skin,

you bear a mystery,
you hold a key,

you have the making of
a whole new tree.

Forbidden Poem

This poem is not for children.
Keep Out!

There is a big oak door
in front of this poem.
It's locked.

And on the door is a notice
in big red letters.
It says: Any child who enters here
will never be the same again.
WARNING. KEEP OUT.

But what's this?
A key in the keyhole.
And what's more,
nobody's about.

'Go on. Look,'
says a little voice
inside your head.
'Surely a poem
cannot strike you dead?'

You turn the key.
The door swings wide.
And then you witness
what's inside.

And from that day
you'll try in vain.
You'll never be the same again.

Pip

Take a tip, pip.

Listen to a word
from a lip, pip.

Find what's found
in the ground.

Don't look back.

Let your shell
crack.

Reach out a root.

Send up a shoot.

Look round for room
to grow and bloom.

Then take a trip, pip.

Puzzled Pea

I'm just a pea
in a plain pea pod.
But there's something about me
that's odd.

For, although like the others,
I'm a plain, green pea,
they are all them . . .
while I'm me.

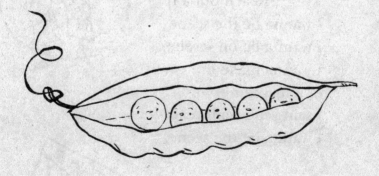

I Wanna Be A Star!

I wanna be a star.
I wanna go far.
I wanna drive around
in a big red car.
I said yeah yeah yeah
I wanna be a star.

I wanna be a hit.
I wanna be it.
I wanna see my name
all brightly lit.
I said yeah yeah yeah
I wanna be a hit.

I wanna be the scene.
I wanna be on screen.
I wanna make the cover
of a magazine.
I said yeah yeah yeah
I wanna be the scene.

I wanna be a star.
I wanna be a star.
But I've only got a job
in a burger bar —
so far . . .

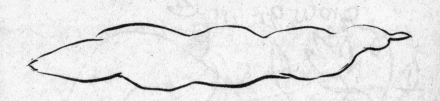

IN MY GARDEN

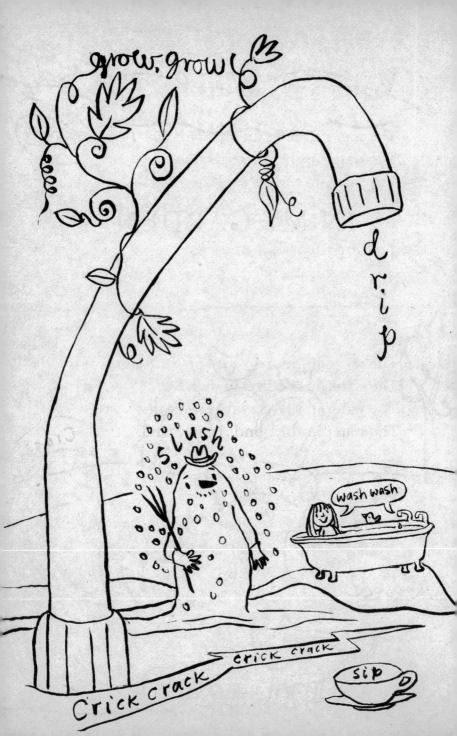

Voices of Water

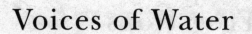

The water in the rain says *Tick Tick Tack*
The water in the sleet says *Slush*
The water in the ice says *Crick Crick Crack*
The water in the snow says *Hush*

The water in the sink says *Slosh Slosh*
The water in the tap says *Drip*
The water in the bath says *Wash Wash*
The water in the cup says *Sip*

The water in the pool says *Splish Splash*
The water in the stream says *Trill*
The water in the sea says *Crish Crash*
The water in the pond . . . stays still.

The water in the soil says *Sow, Sow*
The water in the cloud says *Give*
The water in the plant says *Grow, Grow*
The water in the world says *Live*

Frog Hops

One hop, two hop,
I'm a little frog,

Three hop, four hop,
hopping on a log.

Five hop, six hop,
That's the way to hop.

Seven hop, eight hop,
Wheeeeee . . . PLOP!

PLOP!

Worm Words

'Keep still!'
said Big Worm
to Little Worm.
'You're driving me
round the bend.'

'Don't be daft,'
said Little Worm.
'I'm your other end.'

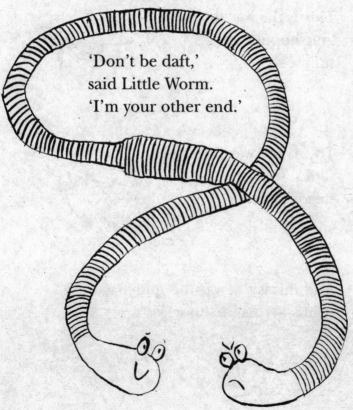

Minibeast Movements

This is the way the beetle stumbles,
clumsy, clockwork, slow.

This is the way the
grasshopper leaps,
so! so! so!

This is the way the snail
slides, smooth,
steady, sure.

And this is the way the spider scuttles,
swiftly across the floor!

Blood Beast

What's that whining,
there in the night?
It must be the creature
with the terrible bite.

It flies through the air
like a vampire beast.
It wants your blood
for a midnight feast.

So hide your head,
fold up your feet
and tuck yourself tightly
under your sheet . . .

It'll get you in the end
wherever you go.
You can't escape
from the mosquieeeeeeeeeeeee . . .
No! It's landing on my toe!

Freak Cat Flea

Hullo, pussies,
come and see.

I'm the heftiest ever
feline flea.

I'm somewhat fat
and six foot three.

So I pity the cat
that catches me.

Emergencies

Red Alert! Red Alert!
I've dropped my lolly in the dirt.

S.O.S! S.O.S!
I've spilled some custard
down my dress.

999! 999!
I'm tangled up
in the washing line.

Ring the alarm! Ring the alarm!
There's an insect landing on my arm.

Bring First Aid! Bring First Aid!
There's a beetle in my lemonade.

Ambulance! And make it quick!
I think I'm going to be sick.

Tiny Diny

Dear, oh dear,
oh, what shall I do?
There's a tiny little dinosaur
in my shoe.

Her teeth are sharp
and her head's like a rock.
When I put my foot in,
she chewed my sock.

Her skin is rough
and her tail is long.
And her ripply muscles
look ever so strong.

And I want to go out,
but what can I do
with a tiny little dinosaur
in my shoe?

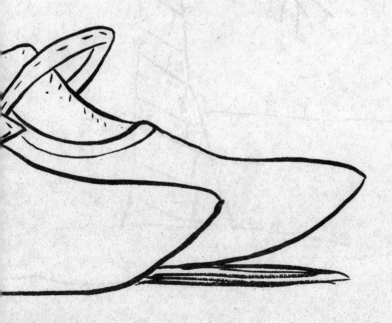

IN MY POCKET

Poem In My Pocket

In my pocket,
feeling round,
what can this be
that I've found?

Pull it out to see
and – oooh!
Look: a poem
just for you.

String

I'm knotty.
I'm grotty.
I'm in a
twisty
tangle.
A piece
of string,
I'm just
the thing
to make
a conker
dangle.

Twang!

I love to stretch
and pluck you – twang!

I pull you back
to flick – f 'tang!

Rubber ribbon,
stretchy strand,

you are my own
e _ _ _ _ _ _ b _ _ _ .

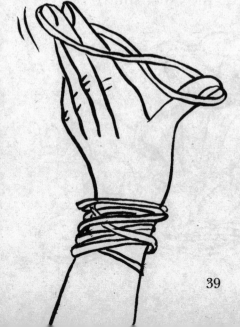

Tissue

Scrumpled up and worn,
a bit tattered and torn,

it's time to put you in the bin –
hmmm . . . can't see one to put you in.

A quick wipe of the nose –
here goes . . .

then back you go, scruff,
with bits and bobs and strands of fluff,

screwed up with all the other stuff.

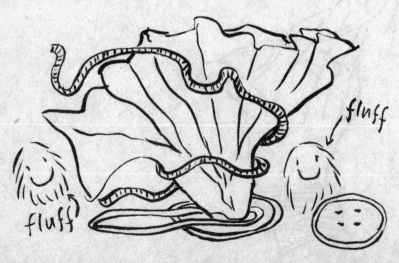

fluff

fluff

Button

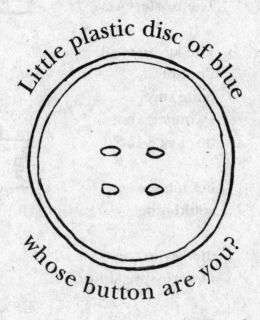

Little plastic disc of blue

whose button are you?

Key

This is the key.
The mystery key.

The key to what?
I'm not
quite sure.
I wonder what
this key is for?

Let me see . . .
could it be:

the key to the door
of a treasure store?

the key to a lid
where things lie hid?

a secret box
with magic locks?

the key to a cupboard,
a closet, a drawer?

I wonder what
this key is for?

When I find it
I'll unlock it,

but meanwhile keep
this key
in my pocket.

Tiny and Shiny

I may be tiny
but I've got grip.

Set me to work
and I rarely slip.

Pages I clamp
with my silver lip.

I am a shiny
p _ _ _ _   c _ _ _ .

Fluff

What's this here?
A piece of fluff.

I don't know where
I get this stuff.

I'll blow it away
with just one puff.

Huff!
There. That's enough.

Shell

Curly, coily
shell,
will you whisper,
will you tell
the spell
that's wound around
or spiralled secretly
inside you?

Tiny, shiny
shell,
I found you
on the beach
and put you
in my pocket
in the hope
that you might teach
to me
strange secrets
of the sea.

Silent shell,
if I listen
will you tell?
Well . . . ?

Coin

It may not be silver, or gold,
but this coin
is a coin that I like to hold.
For here, on the front,
is a tropical tree,
the kind that you get
by a calm, warm sea.
And it seems to me,
that long, long ago
and far, far away
was a place where this coin
could be used to pay
for fruit or for honey
or for bright, fresh fish.

So sometimes I hold it
and dream and wish
I could be on the beach
by that tropical tree,
with long ago, far away
things to see.

AT MY FINGERTIPS:

poems to make me move

Bubblegum Balloon

(Draw a circle in the air to the rhythm of each verse, each circle larger than the previous one. When it bursts, bring your open hands flat onto your face)

Bubblegum, bubblegum,
big pink balloon.

Bubblegum, bubblegum,
round like the moon.

Bubblegum, bubblegum,
planet in space.

Bubblegum bursting
in my face!

Lollipop Poem

This poem's round   *(draw circle in air)*
and it's stuck
on a stick.   *(draw stick below)*

This poem's stripy   *(draw helter skelter line from top to*
                                     bottom)

and nice
to lick.   *(lick!)*

This poem's shiny   *(draw back open palms*
                                    from lollipop)

and sticky   *(touch lollipop)*
and sweet.   *(lick finger and smile: mmm!)*

It's a lollipop poem   *(open hands outward,*
                                    palms upward)

for anyone
to eat.   *(extend hands further out to everyone there)*

That One's Me!

Have you seen a helicopter
hover in the sky?

(raise one hand & hover it in the air)

Have you seen a jet
go screaming by?

(make one hand streak past face)

Have you seen a
submarine glide
beneath the sea?

(make submarine out of hand
with raised thumb/other hand
& forearm can be surface of water)

Have you seen a bicycle?

(mime holding handlebars)

That one's me!

(point to self)

Have you seen a frog as it hops
and leaps?

('hop' one hand along forearm)

Have you seen a slug as it
slowly creeps?

('creep' one hand along forearm)

Have you seen a squirrel as
it scampers up a tree?

(raise arm upright & 'scamper' hand up it)

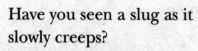

Have you seen a roly-poly?

(whirl both hands round each other)

Have you seen a roly-poly?

That one's me!

(point to self)

Big Boots

These are my boots.
(point to feet on 'These' & 'boots')

They're big.
(make gesture for 'big')

And they're on my feet.
(point to feet on 'on' & 'feet')

You can hear them coming
(one hand to ear, one finger pointing down street)

from the end
(rock head from side to side on 'end' & 'street' to show walking)

of the street.

One's called Betty.

(lift one foot & point to it)

The other's called Fred.

(lift the other & ditto)

And they stand on guard

(fold arms)

at the end

(stern face)

of my bed.

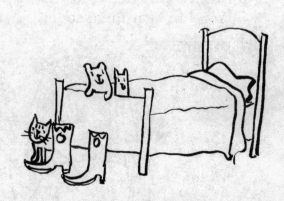

The Web

*(Open hand with fingers stretched out to suggest a spider's web.
Walk, fly or hop each minibeast into the web with the other
hand.)*

In went the beetle.
In went the fly.

In went the bug
with the googly eye.

*(make finger & thumb
circle & put it to one eye)*

In went the ant.
Ppptt! In went the flea.

*(scratch at palm to show
itchy flea sensation)*

'Ah!' said the spider.

*(hold both hands up in
comic menacing way)*

'Here's my tea!'

The Pirate

I've got a telescope.   *(make a telescope with hands held to eye)*

I've got a parrot-bird.   *(wag hand on shoulder)*

I've got a treasure-map   *(make map with palms of both hands)*

which I won't show.   *(hide it to yourself)*

I've got a flag . . .   *(raise arm & waggle hand)*

with a skeleton face on.   *(cross arms & peer over top)*

And I sing:
YO HO HO!   *(shout & wave clenched fist in the air)*

Arabian Nights

Here is a ring
(make ring out of index finger & thumb)

on a silver dish.
(place it on open palm)

Put it on your finger
(put ring on other index finger)

and make a wish.
(throw hands open in wonder)

Here is a genie
who waits in a flask.
(cup both hands, thumbs apart)

If you want a favour

(mime whisper into thumb gap)

whisper and ask.

Here is a carpet

(open hand, palm upwards)

that knows how to fly.

Climb on. Sit tight

(walk first two fingers of other hand onto carpet & pause)

Up into the sky!

(raise carpet, take-off!)

Rickety Train Ride

*(Rock backwards & forwards in time to the train rhythm,
or from side to side for variety)*

I'm riding the train to Ricketywick.
Clickety clickety clack.
I'm sat in my seat
with a sandwich to eat
as I travel the trickety track.

It's an ever so rickety trickety train,
and I honestly thickety think
that before it arrives
at the end of the line
it will tip up my drippety drink.

POEM TO RAP IT UP

Write-A-Rap Rap

Hey, everybody, let's write a rap.
First there's a rhythm you'll need to clap.
Keep that rhythm and stay in time,
'cause a rap needs rhythm and a good
strong rhyme.

The rhyme keeps coming in the very same
place
so don't fall behind and try not to race.
The rhythm keeps the rap on a regular beat
and the rhyme helps to wrap your rap up
neat.

'But what'll we write?'
I hear you shout.
There ain't no rules for
what a rap's about.
You can rap about a robber,
you can rap about a king,
you can rap about a chewed up
piece of string . . .
(well, you can rap about almost . . .
anything!)

You can rap about the ceiling,
you can rap about the floor,
you can rap about the window,
write a rap on the door.
You can rap about things that are
mean or pleasant,
you can rap about wrapping
up a Christmas present.

You can rap about a mystery hidden
in a box,
you can rap about a pair of
smelly old socks.
You can rap about something
that's over and gone,
you can rap about something
going on and on and on and on . . .

But when you think there just ain't nothing
left to say . . .
you can wrap it all up and put it away.
It's a rap. It's a rap. It's a rap rap rap rap
RAP!

THE TALE OF TALES

TONY MITTON
ILLUSTRATED BY PETER BAILEY

Not since the *Jungle Book* has there been
such a wonderful bunch of stories
growing on the story tree.

Join Monkey, Elephant and friends and
travel down the Story Road with them to
Volcano Valley. And as you go, each of the
friends will tell their own special tale.

Come. Come quickly. It's time to set off!

'Great fun, great variety and a great
endorsement of storytelling'
The Irish Times

'An outstanding book . . . A wonderful
collection of the world's stories told
in reverse' *The School Librarian*

DAVID FICKLING BOOKS
0 385 60517 X/978 0 385 60517 5

ONCE UPON A TIDE

TONY MITTON
ILLUSTRATED BY SELINA YOUNG

Down by the seashore
Bess and I
stood on the shingle
and looked at the sky.

I got the needle.
Bess got the thread.
We stitched up a sail
from rags of red.

Tony Mitton and Selina Young have
stitched together a lovely adventure
for young children. ONCE UPON
A TIDE is a bedtime treasure.

'A beautifully told seaside adventure'
Guardian

DAVID FICKLING BOOKS
0 385 60418 1/978 0 385 60418 5

THE QUIGLEYS

Simon Mason

In an ordinary city, in an ordinary street, in an ordinary house, live an ordinary family called . . . THE QUIGLEYS.

Lucy only wants to be a bridesmaid dressed as a bee. Will only wants to be a Harpy Eagle for Christmas. Dad only wants to watch the football in peace. Mum only wants – well, who cares what Mum wants?

But, as with all families, occasionally things do go as planned . . .

'Wonderful snapshots of the chaos and joys of family life' *Guardian*

'Huge fun . . . shows that even families who drive each other bonkers love each other' *Sunday Times*

CORGI YEARLING BOOKS
0 440 86499 2/978 0 440 86499 8

THE QUIGLEYS AT LARGE

SIMON MASON

In an ordinary city, in an ordinary street,
in an ordinary house, live an ordinary
family called . . . THE QUIGLEYS.

Lucy finds a special new friend on
holiday in France. Will finds himself
locked in school at the weekend.
Mum finds herself full of energy at
the local fête. And Dad finds . . .
Well, Dad doesn't find anything.
Dad loses the budgie.

The Quigleys are at large.
Anything could – and does – happen!

'Will make children laugh and
parents wince at the way they can
Get It Wrong' *Sunday Times*

'Enormous charm and warmth' *Guardian*

CORGI YEARLING BOOKS
0 440 86500 X/978 0 440 86500 1

VARJAK PAW

SF SAID

'There are seven skills in the way of Jalal,'
whispered the Elder Paw. 'We know only three
of them. Their names are these. Slow-Time.
Moving Circles. Shadow-Walking.'

Varjak Paw is a Mesopotamian Blue
kitten. He lives high up in an old house
on a hill. He's never left home, until his
grandfather tells him about the Way –
a secret martial art for cats.

Now Varjak must use the Way to survive in
a city full of dangerous dogs, cat gangs, and
strangest of all, the mysterious Vanishings.

'Dazzling' *New York Times*

'Stylish, original and inventive, *Varjak Paw*
is a modern children's classic'
Jacqueline Wilson

CORGI BOOKS
0 552 54818 9/978 0 552 54818 2

THE OUTLAW VARJAK PAW

SF Said

'Varjak Paw,' hissed Sally Bones.
'The cat who thinks he can fight.'

There are seven skills that give a cat
great power, and Varjak Paw knows
them all. He can fight, he can hunt,
he can walk unseen.

There's just one problem. Sally Bones,
the thin white cat who leads the city's
deadliest gang, also knows the skills.
She knows even more than Varjak does.
And now she's coming to get him . . .

*You are an outlaw now, Varjak Paw –
and there's no place left to hide!*

'The cat magic mystique is brilliant'
Richard Adams, author of *Watership Down*

DAVID FICKLING BOOKS
0 385 60755 5/978 0 385 60755 1